SONG INDEXED

You Raise Me Up
The Best Of

Aled Jones

CHESTER MUSIC
part of The Music Sales Group
London / New York / Paris / Sydney / Copenhagen / Berlin / Madrid / Tokyo

Published by
Chester Music Limited
14-15 Berners Street, London, W1T 3LJ, UK.

Exclusive distributors:
Music Sales Limited
Distribution Centre, Newmarket Road,
Bury St Edmunds, Suffolk, IP33 3YB, UK.

Music Sales Pty Limited
120 Rothschild Avenue, Rosebery, NSW 2018, Australia.

Order No. CH72545
ISBN: 978-1-84772-129-7
This book © Copyright 2007 Chester Music Limited.

Edited by Rachel Payne.
Original cover design by Peacock.
Printed in the EU.

www.musicsales.com

Your Guarantee of Quality:

As publishers, we strive to produce every book to
the highest commercial standards.

Particular care has been given to specifying
acid-free, neutral-sized paper made from pulps which
have not been elemental chlorine bleached.

This pulp is from farmed sustainable forests and was
produced with special regard for the environment.

Throughout, the printing and binding have been
planned to ensure a sturdy, attractive publication
which should give years of enjoyment.

If your copy fails to meet our high standards,
please inform us and we will gladly replace it.

YOU RAISE ME UP

Words & Music by Rolf Lovland & Brendan Graham

Lyrics:

When I am down and, oh, my soul so wea-ry, when trou-bles come and my heart bur-dened be, then I am still and wait here in the

si - lence, un - til you come and sit a - while___ with me.

There is no

life, no life with-out it's hun - ger, each rest - less heart beats so im - per - fect -

- ly, but when you come and I am filled with won - der, some-times I

I BELIEVE

Words & Music by Eric Levisalles

11

12

PANIS ANGELICUS

Words: Traditional. Music by César Franck

Arranged by Chris Hazell

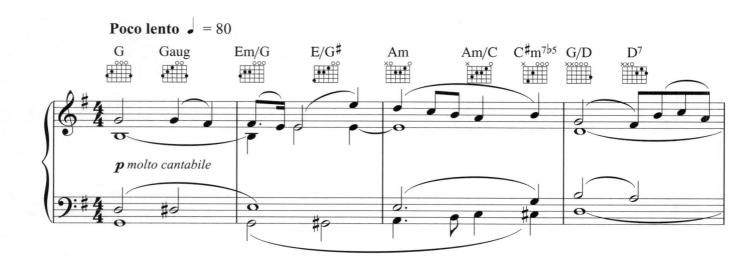

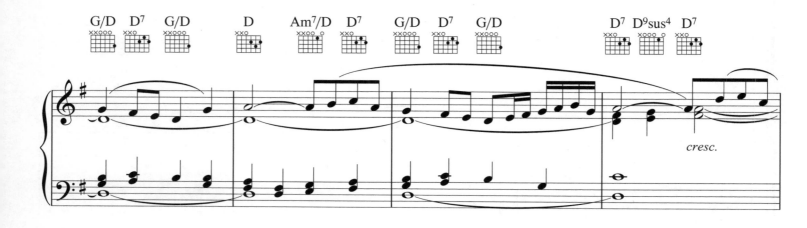

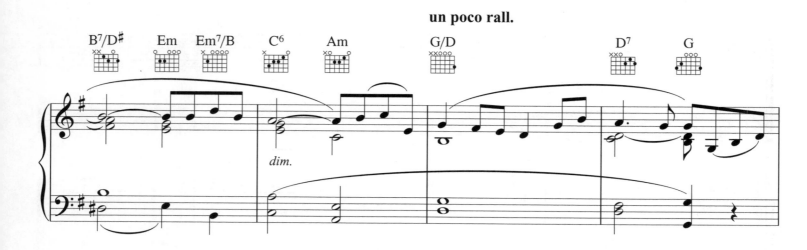

WALKING IN THE AIR
(Theme from 'The Snowman')

Words & Music by Howard Blake

We're walk-ing in the air,_____ we're

float-ing in the moon - lit sky;_____ the peo-ple far be-low are

sleep-ing as we fly._____ I'm

holding ve-ry tight,_____ I'm rid-ing in the mid - night blue._____

I'm hold ing ve-ry tight,_____ I'm

I'm find-ing I can fly   so high a-bovewith you._____

ri-ding in the mid - night blue,   so high a-bovewith you,   ri - ding in the mid - night

blue.

DEEP PEACE (GAELIC BLESSING)

Words: Traditional

Music by John Rutter

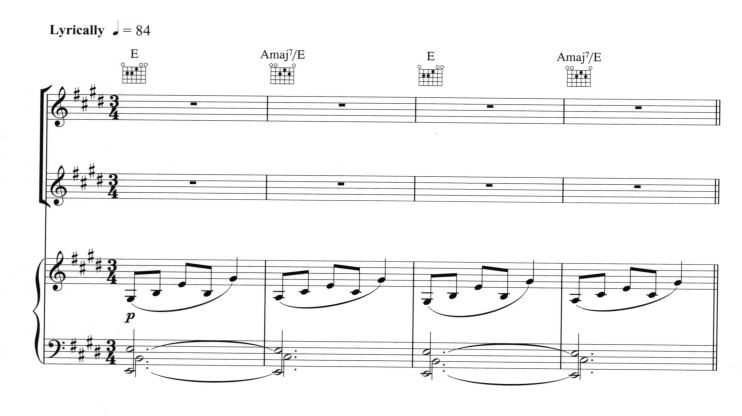

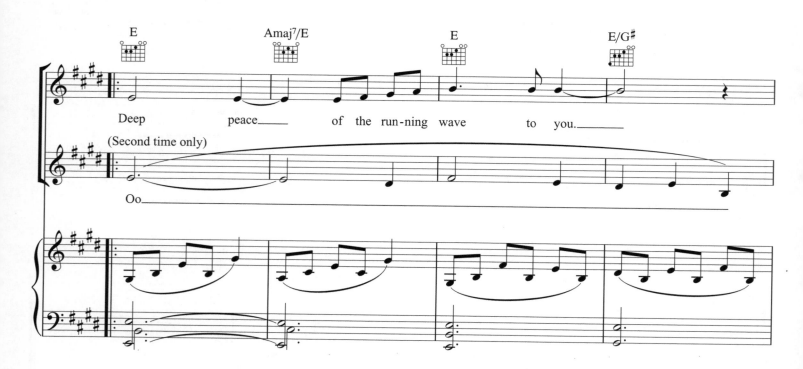

Deep peace___ of the run-ning wave to you.___

(Second time only)

Oo___

28

HOW GREAT THOU ART

Traditional

Arranged by Robert Prizeman

MARBLE HALLS

Traditional

Arranged by Robert Prizeman

dreamt that I dwelt____ in mar - ble halls, with vas - sals and

still___ the same.

SILENT NIGHT

Words by Joseph Mohr. Music by Franz Gruber

Arranged by Robert Prizeman

virgin mother and child, Holy
streams from heaven afar, heav'nly

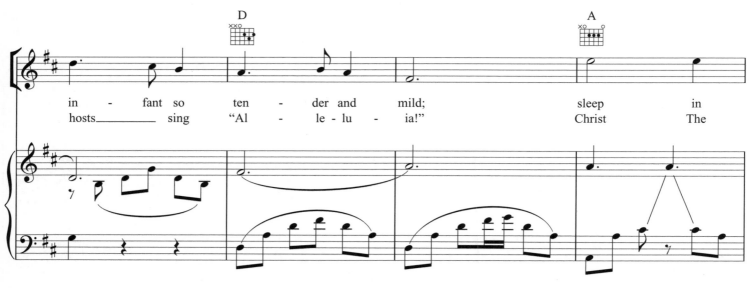

infant so tender and mild; sleep in
hosts sing "Alleluia!" Christ The

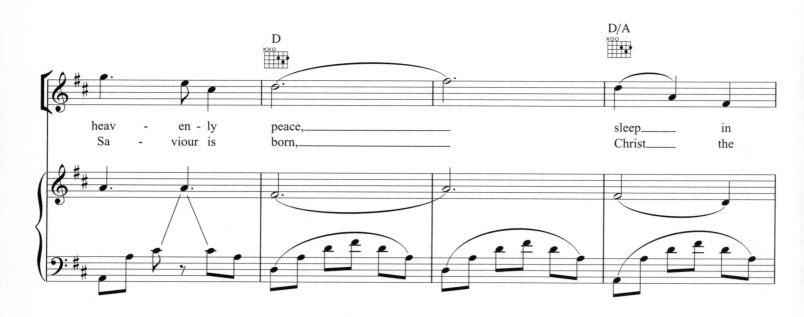

heavenly peace,_____ sleep_____ in
Saviour is born,_____ Christ_____ the

42

44

VESPERA

Words & Music by Robert Prizeman

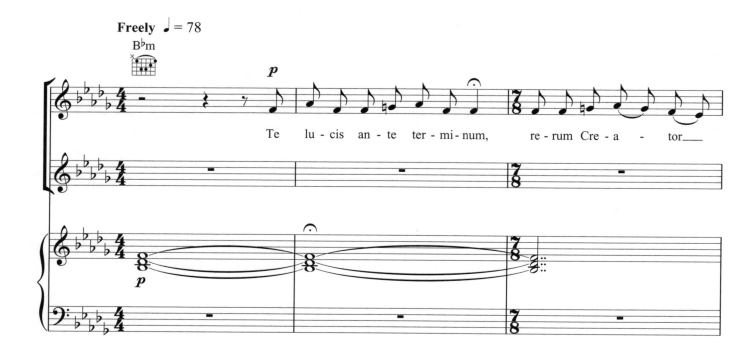

Te lu- cis an - te ter - mi - num, re- rum Cre - a - tor___

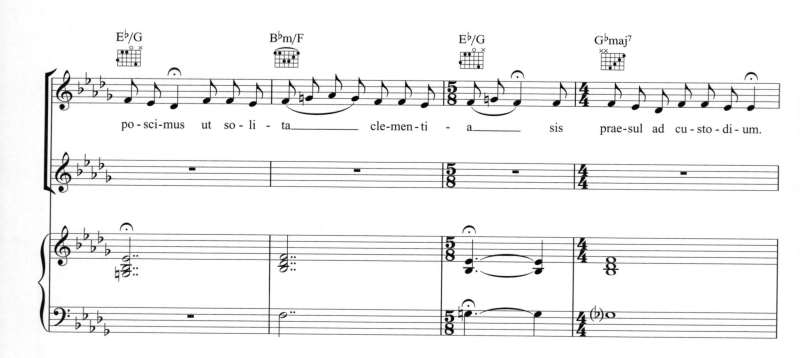

po - sci- mus ut so - li - ta_____ cle - men - ti - a_____ sis prae- sul ad cu - sto - di - um.

ALL THROUGH THE NIGHT
(Ar Hyd y Nos)

Words & Music by Robert Prizeman

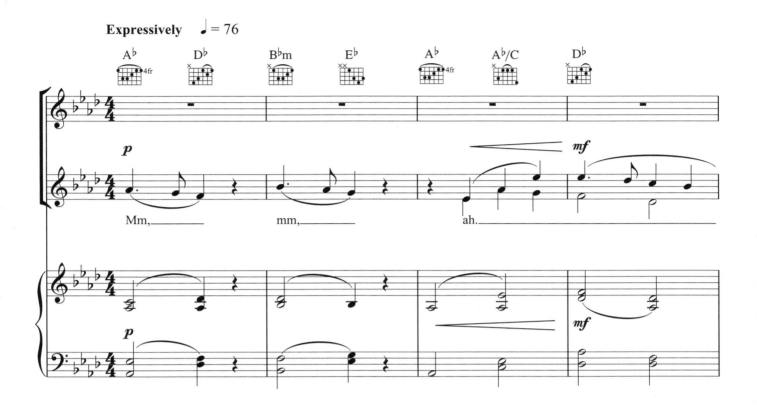

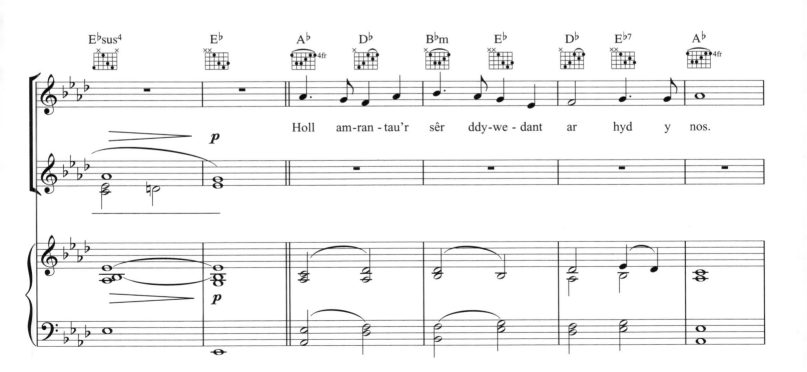

53

PIE JESU

Words: Traditional

Music by John Rutter

Expressively ♩ = 66

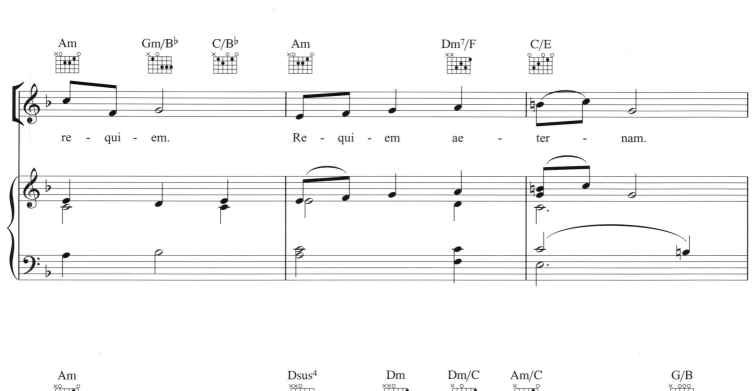

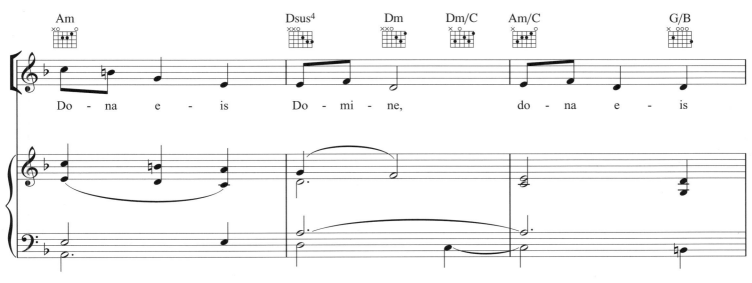

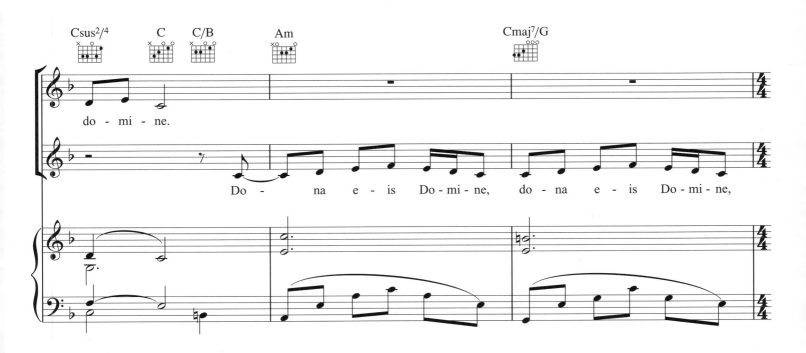

MY LIFE FLOWS ON

Traditional
Arranged by Robert Prizeman

PLACES

(to the 'Out Of Africa' Theme)

Words by Don Black. Music by John Barry

ABIDE WITH ME

Music by W. H. Monk

Arranged by Robert Prizeman

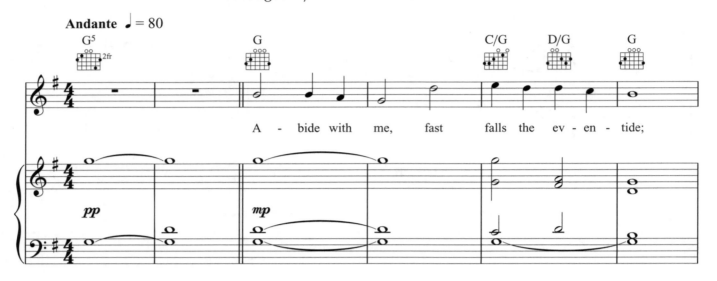

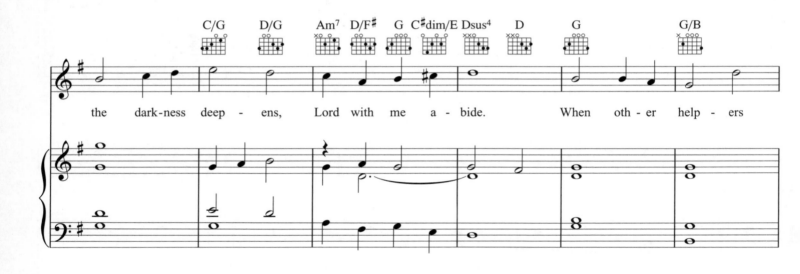

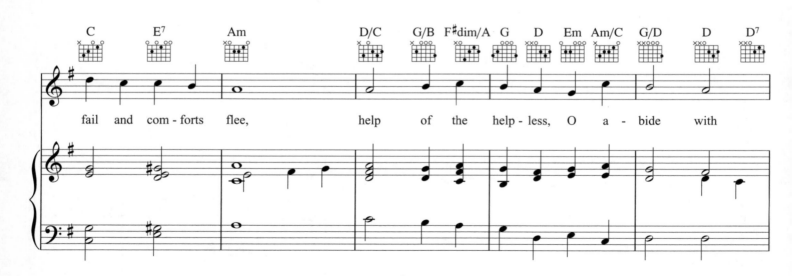

SAN DAMIANO

Words & Music by Sal Solo

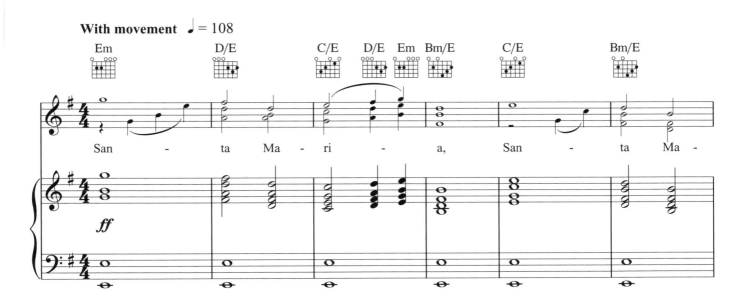

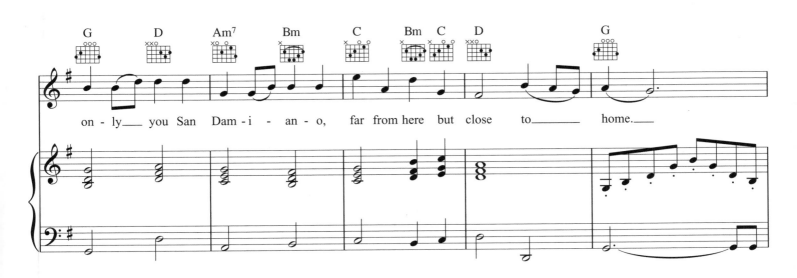

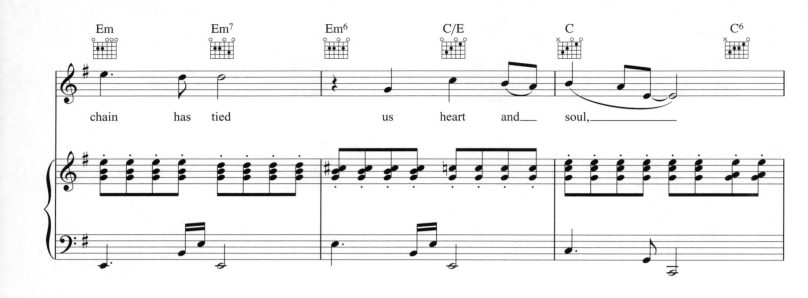

chain has tied us heart and soul,

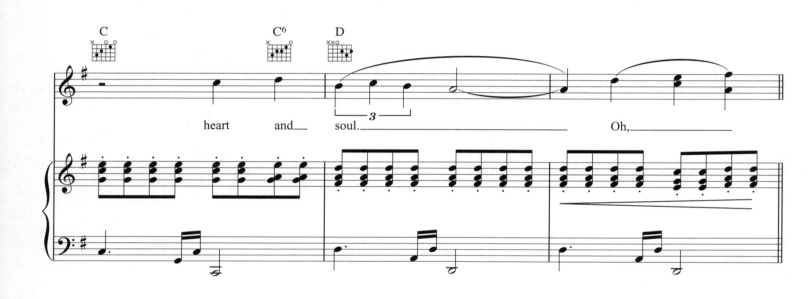

heart and soul. Oh,

on - ly you San Dam - i - an - o, La - dy of the

DID YOU NOT HEAR MY LADY?

Music by George Frideric Handel

Arranged by Robert Prizeman

down the___ gar - den sing - ing? Black - bird and thrush were si - lent, to

hear the___ al - leys ring - ing. Oh, saw you___ not my la - dy out

in the___ gar - den___ there, sham - img the rose and lil - y, for

she is___ twice as fair?

SUO-GAN

Traditional

Arranged by Robert Prizeman

O HOLY NIGHT

Music by Adolphe Adam

Arranged by Robert Prizeman